THE BOOK OF James

GoodMorningGirls.org

The Book of James

Welcome to Good Morning Girls! We are so glad you are joining us.

God created us to walk with Him, to know Him, and to be loved by Him. He is our living well, and when we drink from the water He continually provides, His living water will change the entire course of our lives.

> *Jesus said: "Whoever drinks of the water that I will give him will never be thirsty again. The water that I will give him will become in him a spring of water welling up to eternal life." ~ John 4:14 (ESV)*

So let's begin.

The method we use here at GMG is called the **SOAK** method.

- ❏ **S**—The S stands for ***Scripture***—Read the chapter for the day. Then choose 1-2 verses and write them out word for word. (There is no right or wrong choice—just let the Holy Spirit guide you.)

- ❏ **O**—The O stands for ***Observation***—Look at the verse or verses you wrote out. Write 1 or 2 observations. What stands out to you? What do you learn about the character of God from these verses? Is there a promise, command or teaching?

- ❏ **A**—The A stands for ***Application***—Personalize the verses. What is God saying to you? How can you apply them to your life? Are there any changes you need to make or an action to take?

- ❏ **K**—The K stands for ***Kneeling in Prayer***—Pause, kneel and pray. Confess any sin God has revealed to you today. Praise God for His word. Pray the passage over your own life or someone you love. Ask God to help you live out your applications.

SOAK God's word into your heart and squeeze every bit of nourishment you can out of each day's scripture reading. Soon you will find your life transformed by the renewing of your mind!

Walk with the King!

Courtney

WomenLivingWell.org, GoodMorningGirls.org

Join the GMG Community

Share your daily SOAK at 7:45am on **Facebook.com/GoodMorningGirlsWLW**

Instagram: WomenLivingWell #GoodMorningGirls

GMG Bible Coloring Chart

COLORS	KEYWORDS
PURPLE	God, Jesus, Holy Spirit, Saviour, Messiah
PINK	women of the Bible, family, marriage, parenting, friendship, relationships
RED	love, kindness, mercy, compassion, peace, grace
GREEN	faith, obedience, growth, fruit, salvation, fellowship, repentance
YELLOW	worship, prayer, praise, doctrine, angels, miracles, power of God, blessings
BLUE	wisdom, teaching, instruction, commands
ORANGE	prophecy, history, times, places, kings, genealogies, people, numbers, covenants, vows, visions, oaths, future
BROWN/GRAY	Satan, sin, death, hell, evil, idols, false teachers, hypocrisy, temptation

Introduction to the Book of James

The book of James is considered one of the most practical books of the New Testament. Much like the book of Proverbs in the Old Testament, it focuses on wise Christian living transformed by faith.

James challenges God's people to act like God's people. He stressed that the life of faith touches every area of our lives from trials and temptations, to wisdom and works, to hearing and doing God's word, to controlling our tongues and our desire for money. No stone is left unturned as James addresses every area of a believer's life and pushes them to produce fruit that shows evidence of their faith.

Purpose: To examine ourselves for evidence of faith.

Author: James – the half brother to Jesus.

Time Period: written between AD 44 and 62.

The book of James is likely the first book of the New Testament written. It was written to the Jews, during a time period of great persecution and testing of the church.

Key Verse: James 1:22

"Be doers of the word, and not hearers only."

Major Themes of the Book of James

Testing of Your Faith: James reminds us to consider trials as a joy and he calls the believer to remain steadfast during times of suffering. He exhorts us to trust in God and his sovereignty.

Hearing and Doing the Word: James teaches us that hearers of the word, who do not do the word, are deceived. True, pure religion cares for the orphans and widows.

Faith Without Works is Dead: A true believer produces fruit and evidence of their faith. They do not show partiality to those who are wealthy or well clothed and they display their faith to others, through their good works.

Taming the Tongue: No one can tame the tongue. James challenges us to get control of it.

Wisdom vs. Worldliness: True wisdom comes from God alone and it is shown through our good conduct. Worldliness comes from the enemy and leads to pride and all sorts of division and evil. James reminds us that friendship with the world makes us an enemy of God.

Warning to the Rich: James warns believers against stockpiling our wealth.

The Prayer of Faith: The prayers of a righteous man are powerful. May we live righteously and not forget to use the power that God has given us through prayer!

I cannot wait to take this journey with you through the book of James. I know that we will be challenged to make our faith active through works and be brought to repentance in areas where we have failed. May we surrender our lives to Jesus and allow him to transform us and make us more like Him, for His glory.

19 My brothers, if anyone among you wanders from the truth and someone brings him back, 20 let him know that whoever brings back a sinner from his wandering will save his soul from death and will cover a multitude of sins. ~James 5:19,20

Special Thanks

I want to extend a special thank you to Mandy Kelly, Rosilind Jukic, Bridget Childress and Misty Leask for your help with this journal. Your love, dedication and leadership to the Good Morning Girls ministry is such a blessing to all. Thank you for giving to the Lord.

~ Courtney

Count it all joy, my brothers,

when you meet trials of various kinds,

for you know that the testing of your faith

produces steadfastness.

James 1:2,3

Reflection Question:

Are you in the midst of a trial today? What is the trial and how can you find joy in the middle of the testing of your faith?

James 1:1~18

S—The S stands for *Scripture*

O—The O stands for *Observation*

A—The A stands for *Application*

K—The K stands for *Kneeling in Prayer*

Be doers of the word,

and not hearers only.

James 1:22

Reflection Question:

How do you not only hear and read God's Word but also put it into action in your day-to-day life?

S—The S stands for *Scripture*

O—The O stands for *Observation*

A—The A stands for *Application*

K—The K stands for *Kneeling in Prayer*

You shall love

your neighbor

as yourself.

James 2:8

Reflection Question:

Christians are to not show favoritism based on someone's wealth or nice clothing.

In what ways do you struggle with showing favoritism and loving everyone, as God would have you love them?

S—The S stands for *Scripture*

O—The O stands for *Observation*

A—The A stands for *Application*

K—The K stands for *Kneeling in Prayer*

For as the body

apart from the spirit is dead,

so also faith apart from works is dead.

James 2:26

Reflection Question:

We are reminded that we must show both faith and works throughout all of our Christian walk. In what ways can we do this today?

S—The S stands for **Scripture**

O—The O stands for **Observation**

A—The A stands for **Application**

K—The K stands for **Kneeling in Prayer**

No human being

can tame the tongue.

It is a restless evil,

full of deadly poison.

James 3:8

Reflection Question:

The tongue is capable of both blessing God and cursing people. James says this should not be so.

Has your tongue grown out of control? In what areas do you need to confess your sin to God and make changes?

S—The S stands for *Scripture*

O—The O stands for *Observation*

A—The A stands for *Application*

K—The K stands for *Kneeling in Prayer*

But the wisdom from above is first pure,

then peaceable, gentle, open to reason,

full of mercy and good fruits,

impartial and sincere.

James 3:17

Reflection Question:

Wisdom is a gift from God and reflects the character of God. It leads to godliness.

Are you living wisely? In what areas of your life do you need more wisdom?

S—The S stands for **Scripture**

O—The O stands for **Observation**

A—The A stands for **Application**

K—The K stands for **Kneeling in Prayer**

What causes quarrels

and what causes fights among you?

Is it not this, that your passions

are at war within you?

James 4:1

Reflection Question:

Do you have a strained relationship with someone close to you in your life? Why is there tension between you two?

In what ways can you safeguard yourself from confusing your own personal desires with God's desires?

S—The S stands for *Scripture*

O—The O stands for *Observation*

A—The A stands for *Application*

K—The K stands for *Kneeling in Prayer*

Whoever knows the right thing to do

and fails to do it,

for him it is sin.

James 4:17

Reflection Question:

Is there an area in your life where you know what to do but are not doing it?

What changes do you need to make today to avoid sin in your life?

James 4:13~17

S—The S stands for *Scripture*

O—The O stands for *Observation*

A—The A stands for *Application*

K—The K stands for *Kneeling in Prayer*

Above all, do not swear,

either by heaven or by earth

or by any other oath,

but let your "yes" be yes

and your "no" be no.

James 5:12

Reflection Question:

A Christian should be trustworthy and a person of their word.

Do you struggle with keeping your word? Is there a promise you need to follow through on or someone you need to apologize to, for a broken promise?

James 5:1-12

S—The S stands for *Scripture*

O—The O stands for *Observation*

A—The A stands for *Application*

K—The K stands for *Kneeling in Prayer*

The prayer of a righteous person

has great power as it is working.

James 5:16

Reflection Question:

James tells us there is great power in the prayers of a righteous person.

Have you neglected your prayer life? How have you seen the power of God displayed through your prayers?

James 5:13~19

S—The S stands for *Scripture*

O—The O stands for *Observation*

A—The A stands for *Application*

K—The K stands for *Kneeling in Prayer*

55597334R00019

Made in the USA
Lexington, KY
28 September 2016